D1604079

1

A Kid's Guide to Baptism

So you want to be baptized. That's great! Baptism is a HUGE milestone in the life of a Christian, but it is not something we just do because everyone else is doing it.

Before you are baptized, you need to understand what you are doing. You should be able to explain what baptism means, and you should also be able to say why you want to be baptized.

This book will help you do that. As you work through these pages you will be preparing yourself to take a big step forward in your faith journey.

What is baptism?

- Baptism means to *immerse* (as in water)
- It is something you do to show other people you love Jesus, you want to obey his commands, and you have asked him to forgive you.
- It is a symbol of Jesus dying, being buried and raising from the grave.

What is a symbol?

A symbol is an image or an object that stands for something else.

For example, what does the $ symbol represent? Yes, that is the symbol for a dollar. What about a bald eagle? If you said it is a symbol of freedom or America, you are right.

Take a minute and see how many symbols you can list.

_____

_____

_____

_____

_____

_____

Here is another way to think about it. If you were to wear a sports jersey, that does not mean you are a professional player. For a basketball player, the jersey is part of the uniform to show what team he or she plays for.

You are not a part of a professional team just because you wear a jersey. The opposite is also true – if a professional player does not wear the jersey, it does not mean they are no longer part of the team.

Someone is not automatically forgiven of sins and a member of "Team Jesus" just because they are baptized. You have to repent and ask Jesus to forgive you in order have eternal life on "Team Jesus".

Baptism is a symbol of being on Jesus' "team". We do it to show everyone that we are on his team. Being forgiven and making Him our Savior gets us on his team. We can be forgiven and not baptized. We can get baptized but that does not make us forgiven. Baptism is something we do to show others that we have been forgiven and have put our trust in Jesus.

A wedding ring is another good example of a symbol that can help you understand baptism. When a husband and wife get married, they usually exchange rings as symbols of their love for each other. When they wear their ring, it is a symbol to let everyone else know they are married. Wearing a ring does not automatically mean you are married, just like if a married person takes their ring off, it does not mean they are no longer married. The rings are symbolic of their marriage. A married person wears their ring to show people they are married, just like someone getting baptized does so to show everyone Jesus forgave them, and they are choosing to follow Him.

When you are baptized, you are submerged in water, meaning you go all the way under. (Don't worry, you can plug your nose if you need to!)

Going under water and coming out of the water is symbolic as well.

We were therefore buried with him through baptism into death in order that, just as Christ was raised from the dead through the glory of the Father, we too may live a new life. Romans 6:24 (NIV)

When you are lowered into the water it is a symbol of putting sin to death. Jesus died and was buried so we could be forgiven of our sin. Going under the water is a reminder of His death and showing everyone that your sins have been buried.

Jesus did not stay dead though. He was only dead for three days, then He rose from the grave. That's what we celebrate every year at Easter - Jesus' resurrection.

When you come up out of the water it is a reminder of your new life in Christ.

Therefore, if anyone is in Christ, the new creation has come: The old has gone, the new is here!
2 Corinthians 5:17 (NIV)

Why should you be baptized?

Here are a few reasons you should consider being baptized.

- ***Jesus himself was baptized.***

Look up and read Matthew 3:12-17, then answer the questions.

Who baptized Jesus?

_____

_____

_____

What happened after Jesus was baptized?

_____

_____

_____

How did God feel when Jesus was baptized?

_____

_____

_____

- ### *Jesus tells us to be baptized*

Look up and read Matthew 28:16-20, then answer the questions.

Who was Jesus talking to?

_____

_____

_____

What did he tell them to do?

_____

_____

_____

How do you know if you are ready to be baptized?

In the Bible when someone is baptized, they 'repent' first. Baptism comes after your choice to follow Jesus and is a way to show your friends and family that you trust Jesus and have asked him to forgive you and to be your Savior.

Questions to ask before you are baptized:

#1 Have you asked Jesus to forgive you?

_____

#2 Are you ready to tell/show your friends and family that Jesus is your Savior? Who are some people you would tell when you get baptized?

_____

_____

_____

_____

_____

Being Clothed with Christ

So in Christ Jesus you are all children of God through faith, for all of you who were baptized into Christ have clothed yourselves with Christ. Galatians 3:26-27 (NIV)

What do you think it means to "have clothed yourselves with Christ"?

_____

_____

_____

_____

_____

_____

_____

_____

Think about when you get dressed in the morning. You take off your pajamas, then you put on the clothes you plan to wear for the day.

When you are 'clothed with Christ' it means you recognize you are a sinful person. You have asked Jesus to forgive you of your sins. You 'take off' old habits that are not pleasing to God. You work to change your behavior to live a life the way God would want you to live.

You 'put on' the Armor of God. You 'put on' the Fruit of the Spirit. Being baptized means you are making a public declaration that you are going to live your life for God. It will not be easy, and you will make mistakes along the way. But being 'clothed with Christ' means you love God, and you want to follow Him.

Fruit of the Spirit

²² But the fruit of the Spirit is love, joy, peace, forbearance, kindness, goodness, faithfulness, ²³ gentleness and self-control. Against such things there is no law. ²⁴ Those who belong to Christ Jesus have crucified the flesh with its passions and desires. ²⁵ Since we live by the Spirit, let us keep in step with the Spirit. ²⁶ Let us not become conceited, provoking and envying each other.
Galatians 5:22-26 (NIV)

On the pages that follow, take some time to write out what these "fruits" could look like in your life. What are some things you could say and do that would show those around you that you are a Christian and living your live the way Jesus wants you to? (if you don't know what the following words means, you can look it up, or ask an adult or your pastor)

Love

_____

_____

_____

_____

_____

Joy

_____

_____

_____

_____

_____

Peace

_____

_____

_____

_____

_____

_____

Forbearance (patience)

_____

_____

_____

_____

_____

_____

Kindness

_____

_____

_____

_____

_____

Goodness

_____

_____

_____

_____

_____

Faithfulness

_____

_____

_____

_____

_____

Gentleness

_____

_____

_____

_____

_____

Self-control

_____

_____

_____

_____

_____

_____

Here are some questions to discuss with your parents and pastor to help you determine if now is the time for you to be baptized.

Are you ready to be baptized?

In your own words, what is baptism?

_____

_____

_____

_____

_____

_____

_____

Why do you want to be baptized?

_____

_____

_____

_____

_____

In your own words, describe your relationship with
Jesus.

_____

_____

_____

_____

_____

How do you know you are ready to be baptized?

_____

_____

_____

_____

_____

_____

_____

_____

_____

_____

_____

Your testimony

Have you ever seen a courtroom trial in session? Maybe on a TV show? During a trial, there are often witnesses who are called to the stand to testify. That means they give their version of events to the rest of the courtroom. The lawyers are trying to build their case, and they need to gather facts about the case from the testimony of people who know what happened.

A testimony is a personal account of events.

When you are baptized, you may have an opportunity to share your personal testimony with those who are watching.

What is a personal testimony? A personal testimony is a story about your experience with Jesus. When you are baptized you may have an opportunity to share what Jesus has done in your life.

Read Acts 9:1-31

This is the account of Jesus speaking to Saul on the Road to Damascus. Saul was a pretty bad guy – he persecuted and killed Christians. But one day he had an encounter with Jesus and his life changed. His life changed so much that he even changed his name to Paul!

Paul was later arrested for preaching about Jesus. On his way to jail, he was given an opportunity to speak to the crowd and defend himself, and he gave his testimony about how Jesus had changed his life.

Read Acts 22:1-21

What was Paul like before Jesus spoke to him on the Road to Damascus?

_____

_____

_____

_____

_____

_____

What did Ananias tell Saul?

_____

_____

_____

_____

_____

What did Saul do after he was baptized?

_____

_____

_____

_____

_____

Reading through Paul's defense, we can see he is actually sharing his personal testimony.

He tells what his life was like before Jesus, how he met Jesus, and what his life was like after.

The following questions will help to help you follow Paul's example and guide you in writing out your personal testimony.

How was your life before you asked Jesus to forgive you? How was your attitude? How did you treat people?

_____

_____

_____

_____

_____

_____

_____

_____

_____

_____

Explain when you prayed and asked Jesus to forgive you. Where were you? Was anyone with you? Why did you make that decision?

_____

_____

_____

_____

_____

_____

_____

_____

_____

_____

_____

How is your life with Jesus now? How is it different than it was before you committed your life to Him? Do people notice you are nicer, more patient, and more loving? (think of the Fruit of the Spirit)

_____

_____

_____

_____

_____

_____

_____

_____

_____

_____

Congratulations on completing your workbook!

Baptism is a big step in your Christian life, and I am glad you took the time to work through these pages to help you prepare.

Now it is time for you to talk to your pastor about the next steps. You will probably be asked some of the questions you answered here in this book, so if you answered them all there is a good chance you are ready!

As I wrote these pages, I prayed specifically for YOU so you would know for sure you were ready to be baptized.

May you continue to grow closer to God as you follow His path for your life!

Day of your baptism

Today is your big day! Baptism is a milestone in the life of a Christian. It is a moment you will remember forever. The next few pages will give you spaces to write down some things that will be good for you to remember on the day you are baptized.

How have you felt since you decided you wanted to be baptized? (nervous, scared, happy...)

_____

_____

_____

_____

_____

_____

Ask some people who love you to write a few words of encouragement for you to remember.

_____

_____

_____

_____

_____

_____

_____

_____

_____

_____

_____

_____

What was your actual baptism experience like?

_____

_____

_____

_____

_____

_____

_____

_____

_____

_____

After baptism

Now that you have been baptized, how do you feel?

_____

_____

_____

_____

_____

Who came to watch you be baptized?

_____

_____

_____

_____

_____

Certificate of Baptism

This certifies that

_____

was obedient to Scripture and was baptized in the name of
the Father, the Son, and the Holy Spirit

*on*_____   *at* _____

_____
Pastor

*Therefore go and make disciples of all nations, baptizing them
in the name of the Father, and of the Son, and of the Holy
Spirit*

Matthew 28:19

Additional Notes

About the Author

I am happily married to my best friend, and dad to the greatest daughter anyone could have. I have spent the better part of 20 years in doing some kind of kid's ministry. I've done it all: everything from teaching in a private school, substitute teaching in public schools, full time kids pastor, part time kids pastor, and even volunteering.

My Journey

I studied Spanish throughout high school, and began to feel like I wanted to be a teacher, so when I got to college I studied Spanish for elementary education. I spent two summer internships in Central America doing kids ministry mission work. Over the years I have led and translated for multiple mission trips and VBS weeks in the US, Central America and South America.

While still in college, through a series of events that only God could have orchestrated, I was offered a position teaching Spanish K-8 in a private Christian school. After several years of teaching, and God solidifying a calling to ministry to kids, I moved into a full-time children's/youth pastor position. From there ministry has had its ups and downs. I have been full time children's pastor, volunteer children's pastor, and volunteer under other children's pastors. I have been in large churches, small churches, and church plants. I am currently not actively involved in local children's ministry, which has allowed me time to concentrate on writing resources (like this one!) to help kids, those so serve locally in children's ministry, as well as parents.

If you liked A **Kid's Guide to Baptism,** you should check out some of the other resources I created --

Got Fruit: a guide to family devotions is a great, short devotional that you can do on your own, or with your family. It is on Amazon for Kindle and has made it to #1 on the kid's ministry book lists.

Prayer Pact: a 30 day prayer journal for kids is a great way to help kids read scripture and begin forming a habit of prayer in their life/

Check out my website for more info on these great resources and many more.

pastorronbrooks.com

Made in the USA
Las Vegas, NV
22 June 2023

73773448R00026